Fiesta

By Maria Fleming

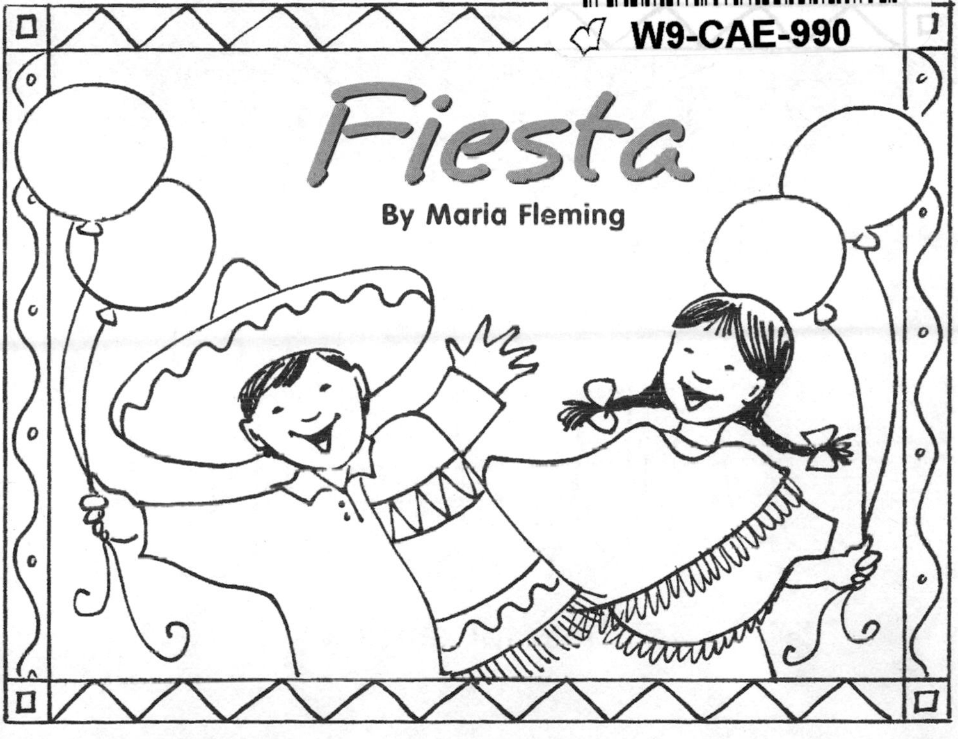

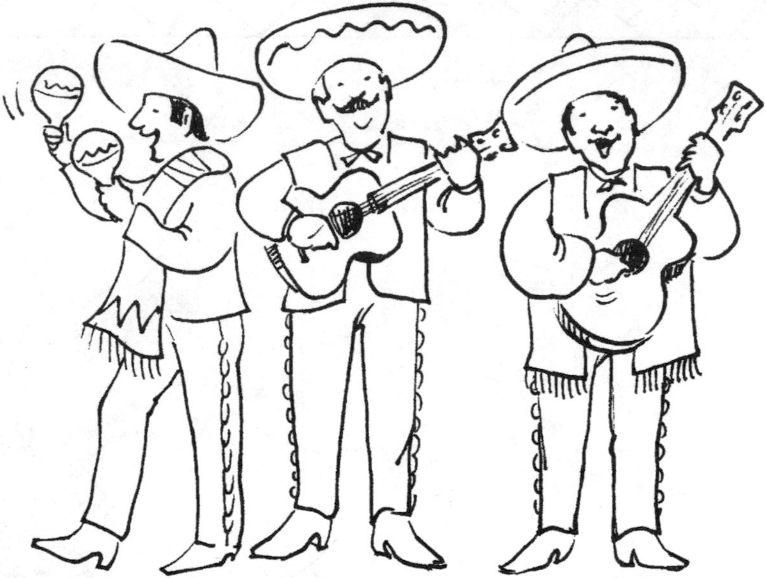

Time for music.

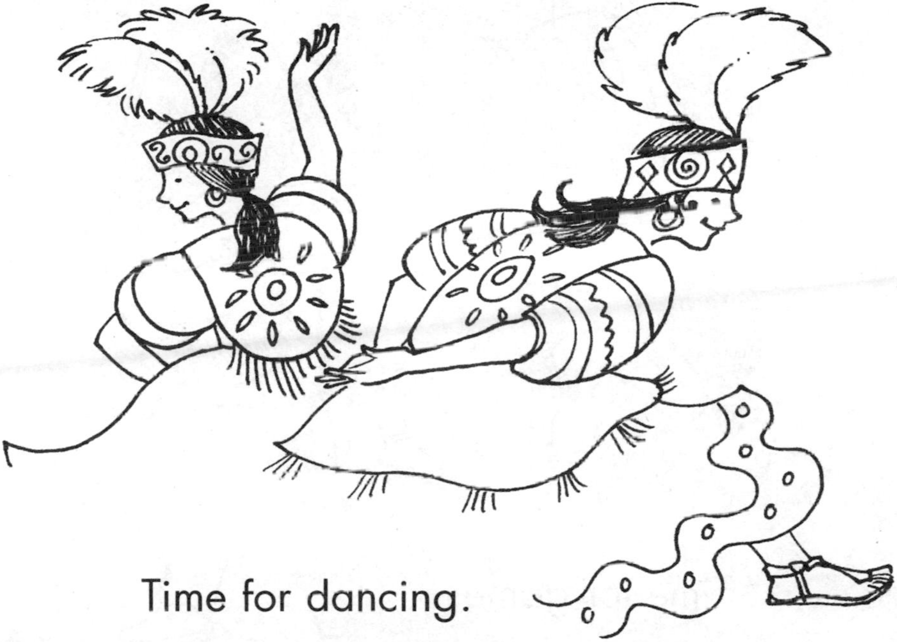

Time for dancing.

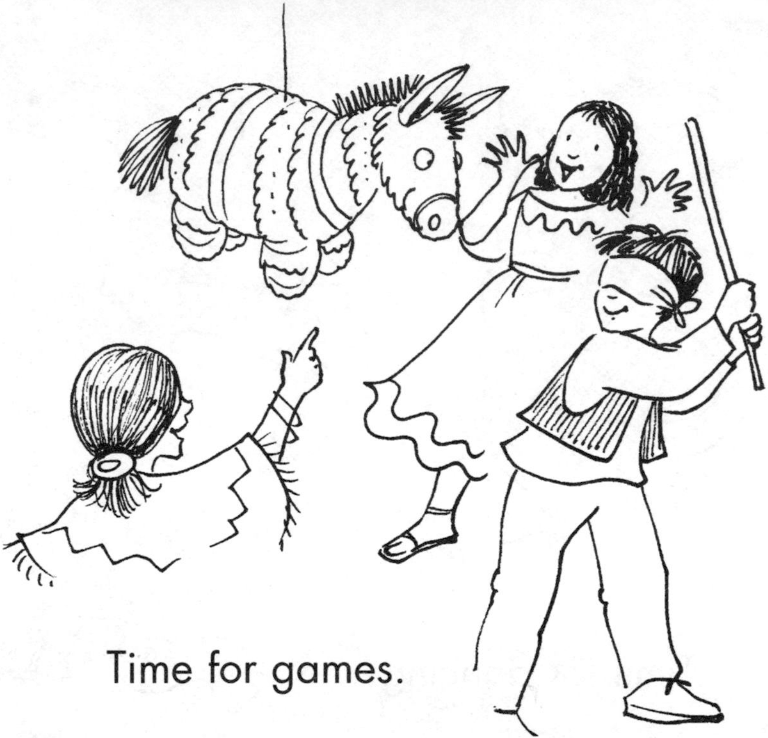

Time for games.

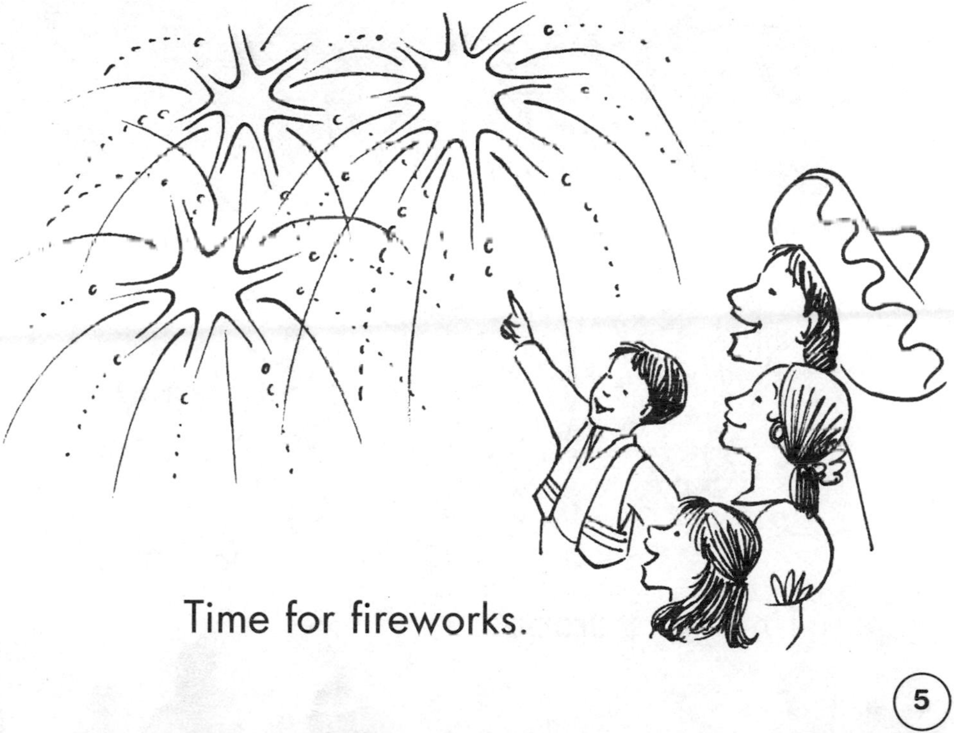

Time for fireworks.

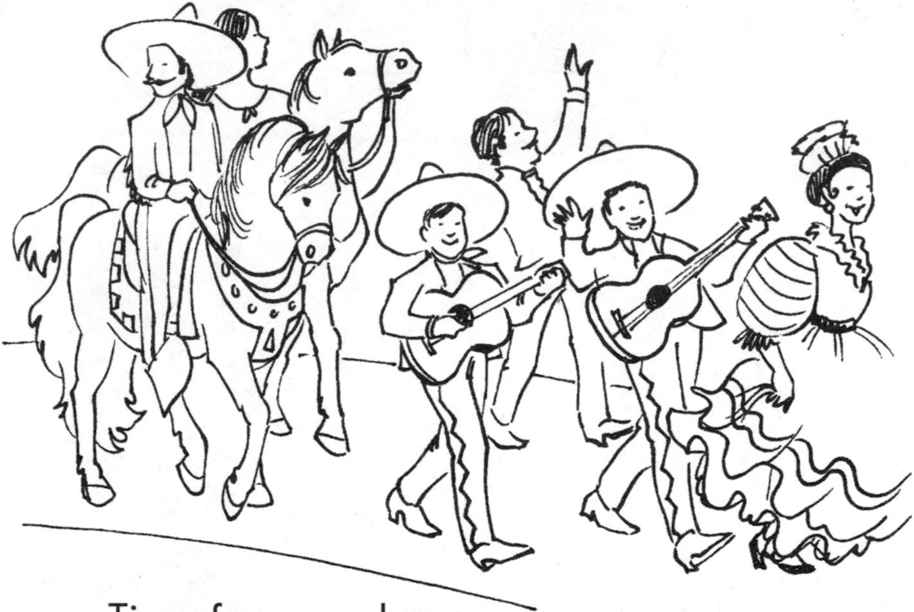

Time for parades.

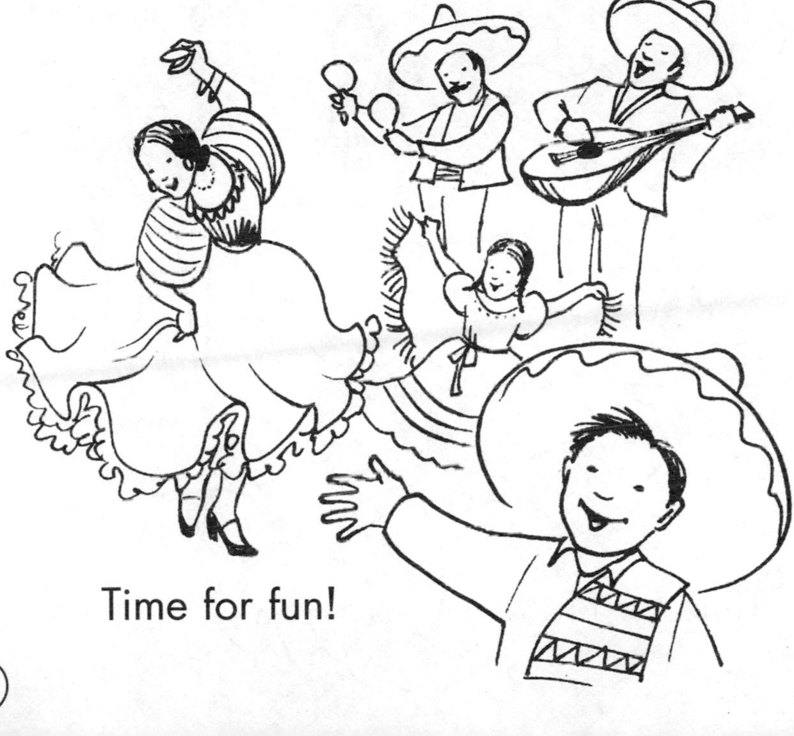

Time for fun!

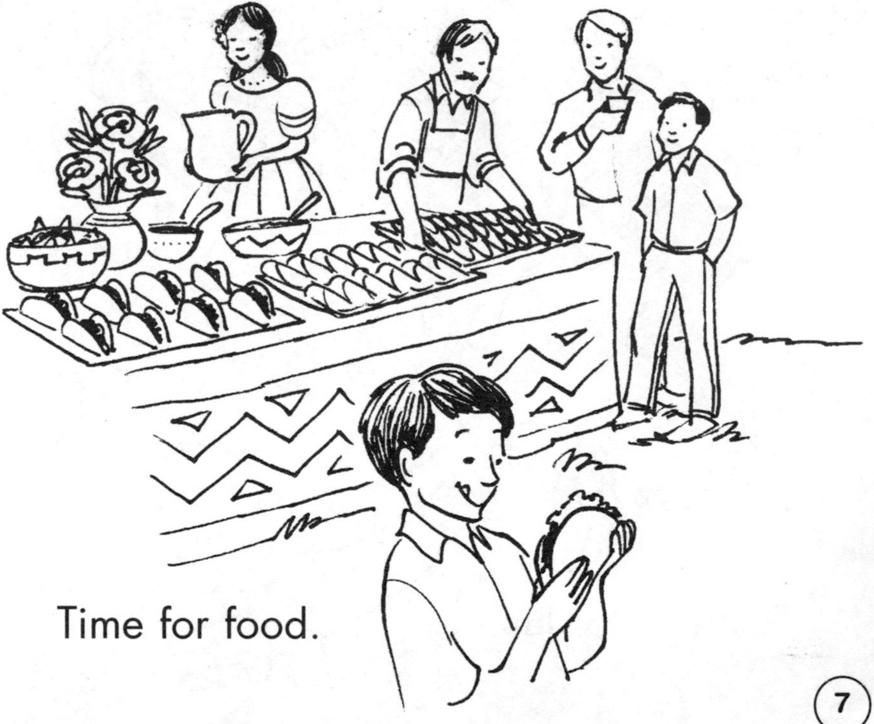

Time for food.